The **QR** Book

by Lynn Maslen Kertell
pictures by Sue Hendra and John R. Maslen

Scholastic Inc.
New York • Toronto • London • Auckland • Sydney • Mexico City • New Delhi • Hong Kong • Buenos Aires

Queen

quails

Quails cover the queen

with a cozy quilt.

Rainbow

rooster

Rabbits and raccoons

rumba in the rain.

The queen likes to

rock and roll!

Look for these q and r words in this book.

quails	rabbits
queen	raccoons
quilt	rain
	rainbow
	rock and roll
	rooster
	rumba

Look for these additional **q** and **r** words in the pictures: quarter, question mark, radio, raindrops, ridge, and road.